Yves C. Ton-That • Michael Weinhaus

GOLF RULES CARTOONS

Register for free at **www.tomandchip.com** and we will
keep you posted about any changes to the rules of golf.

Dear golfer,

Who really likes learning the rules of golf? To most people, they seem dreary and complicated. This is why we have created Tom & Chip. The two main characters in our comic strip love golf even though they are not exactly talented and their knowledge of the rules is somewhat lacking. In 80 cartoons, they have all sorts of adventures and stumble from one predicament to the next. Using these situations, we hope to remind you of the most important rules and to familiarize you with some other interesting ones that you may not yet be aware of. Always in an easy-to-understand and amusing way. After meeting Tom and Chip, you will be surprised to find out that learning the rules of golf really can be fun!

We hope you enjoy reading our book and wish you a great time on the golf course.

Yves C. Ton-That and Michael Weinhaus

PS: Underneath each cartoon, you will find the rule number in case you want to look it up in the official rule book.

Yves C. Ton-That

Author and Publisher

Yves C. Ton-That has been a rules official for more than 25 years. He has written ten books on golf which have been translated into more than 20 languages. His "Golf Rules Quick Reference" is an award winner, and with more than 2.5 million copies sold, it is the best-selling golf book in the world. He lives and works in Zurich, Switzerland.

Michael Weinhaus

Author

Michael Weinhaus is a USGA Rules of Golf Expert with more than two decades of refereeing experience. He has co-authored in excess of 2000 questions for a rules quiz and is a former PGA of America Executive Director Gateway Section. He lives and works in St. Louis, Missouri USA.

Dusan Reljic

Illustrator

Dusan Reljic is a comic strip author and cartoonist with a vast portfolio. In more than 40 years, he has authored numerous comic series and worked internationally for major newspapers and magazines. He lives and works in Belgrade, Serbia.

TABLE OF CONTENTS

Publisher:
Artigo Publishing International
Artigo LLC
Seestrasse 489
8038 Zurich
Switzerland
Telephone: +41-43-3215555
Fax: +41-43-3215556
E-mail: info@expertgolf.com
www.expertgolf.com

Text/concept:
Yves C. Ton-That/Michael Weinhaus

Illustrations:
Dusan Reljic

ISBN 978-3-906852-36-2

1st edition 2022

TEE

SITUATION: **Chip has a special present for his buddy Tom ...**

QUESTION: **Is Chip right that it's mandatory for every player to carry a rule book during the round?**

ANSWER: It's not mandatory, but all players are responsible for knowing and applying the rules correctly. A great alternative to the official rule book is the handy "Golf Rules Quick Reference" guide by Expert Golf; it's very easy to understand and answers virtually every rules question in a matter of seconds.

Rule 1.3b(1).

SITUATION: **Tom brings some clubs that he wants to test ...**

QUESTION: **What's the maximum number of clubs allowed, and what's the penalty for carrying too many?**

ANSWER: The rules allow a maximum of 14 clubs. If a player begins their round with more than this, they must declare the extra clubs out of play once they become aware of the breach. In stroke play, they'll be penalized 2 strokes per hole, with a maximum of 4 strokes per round.

Rule 4.1b.

SITUATION: **Chip's teeing up his ball in an unusual place ...**

QUESTION: **Is Chip right that teeing the ball up behind the tee-markers as far back as you like is allowed?**

ANSWER: The teeing area extends to 2 club-lengths behind the markers, and the ball must be played from within this area. Neither teeing off in front of the markers nor farther back than 2 club-lengths is allowed.

Rule 6.1b and definition "Teeing Area."

SITUATION: **Tom and Chip's tee time is at 10.00 a.m. ...**

QUESTION: **What's the penalty for teeing off late, and what about starting early?**

ANSWER: If a player starts their round up to 5 minutes late, they usually get 2 penalty strokes in stroke play. If they're more than 5 minutes late, they're usually disqualified. The same applies to starting early. If Tom tees off 2 minutes before his tee time, he'll get a 2-stroke penalty.

Rule 5.3a.

SITUATION: **Chip hits his ball right at the flag ...**

QUESTION: **Is there a penalty, and if so, what is it?**

ANSWER: Tom gets 2 penalty strokes in stroke play for asking for advice while Chip's not penalized because he didn't answer Tom and didn't show him which club he used.

Rule 10.2a.

SITUATION: **Just when Tom's about to tee off, the greenkeeper's cat crosses the street …**

QUESTION: **Does Tom's air shot count as a stroke?**

ANSWER: Tom intended to strike the ball, therefore his swing counts as a stroke. Distractions are part of the game and don't entitle a player to replay a shot.

Definition "Stroke."

SITUATION: **Tom misses his ball on the first tee ...**

QUESTION: **Does it count as a stroke if the ball remains in the teeing area? And is Tom allowed to tee the ball up again?**

ANSWER: Every swing at the ball with the intention of striking it counts as a stroke. Because the ball's still lying within the teeing area, Tom may place it on the tee again or even tee it up in a different place within the teeing area.

Rule 6.2b(6) and definition "Stroke."

FAIRWAY AND ROUGH

SITUATION: **Tom hooks his ball into high grass ...**

QUESTION: **Is Tom allowed to play the ball from its new position? And will Chip be penalized for moving Tom's ball?**

ANSWER: Tom's ball must be put back on its original spot. If Tom and Chip can't determine the exact spot, they must estimate it. There's no penalty for accidentally moving a ball during a search.

Rule 7.4.

SITUATION: **Chip's ball comes to rest in a tree high above the ground ...**

QUESTION: **Is Chip allowed to use Tom's putter for the remaining holes?**

ANSWER: No, making a stroke with a club which is used by another person playing on the course isn't permitted.

Rule 4.1b(2).

SITUATION: **After Chip's ball comes to rest on the fairway, he sees a dog sniffing at it ...**

HEY ... WHAT'S THAT DOG DOING?

HE PICKED UP MY BALL!

COME BACK HERE WITH MY BALL!

© Artigo Publishing

QUESTION: **Where does Chip have to play from, and what happens if he doesn't manage to get his ball back?**

ANSWER: Chip's ball at rest was moved by an "outside influence." Chip must replace the ball on its original spot without penalty. If he doesn't know the original spot, he must estimate it. In the event that the ball can't be recovered, Chip may use another ball.

Rules 4.2c(2), 9.6, 14.2a and definition "Outside Influence."

SITUATION: **Tom notices that a big clump of mud is stuck to the ball ...**

QUESTION: **Is Tom allowed to remove the mud from his ball?**

ANSWER: Tom isn't allowed to clean his ball unless it's necessary for identification purposes. In that case, he must mark, then lift the ball and not clean it more than needed to identify it.

Rules 9.1a, 7.3 and 14.1c.

SITUATION: **For the perfect stroke, Tom needs to know the exact distance to the hole ...**

QUESTION: **Is Tom allowed to ask Chip for distance information, and what happens if Chip answers – is that illegal advice?**

ANSWER: Public information such as distances is not advice. Tom may ask Chip how far he's away from the hole and Chip may answer without penalty. Advice as defined in the rules would be a comment that's intended to influence a player in choosing a club or making a stroke, or in how they play a hole or a round.

Rule 10.2a and definition "Advice."

SITUATION: **Tom's ball comes to rest between lots of worm casts …**

QUESTION: **Is Tom allowed to remove the worm casts without penalty?**

ANSWER: Worm casts are classed as "loose impediments" and can be removed anywhere without penalty. However, Tom must pay attention that his ball doesn't move in doing so; otherwise, he would have to put it back with 1 penalty stroke.

Rule 15.1 and definition "Loose Impediment."

SITUATION: **Chip's ball lands under a tree where a branch is in his way ...**

QUESTION: **Is Chip right that bending a branch is allowed, while breaking it would result in a penalty?**

ANSWER: The rules don't only prohibit breaking a branch but also bending it out of the way, if this improves the conditions for the stroke.

Rule 8.1a.

SITUATION: **Chip finds his ball in the semi-rough but what he sees scares him half to death ...**

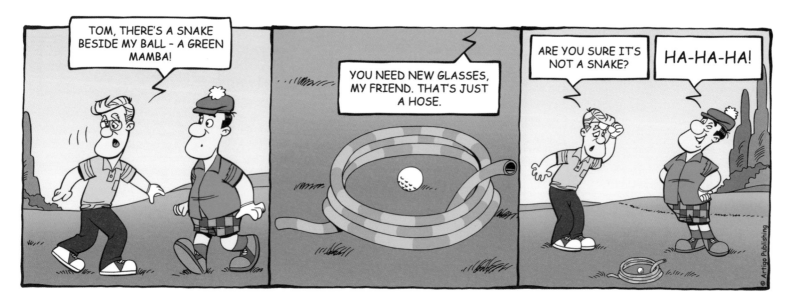

QUESTION: **Is Chip allowed to remove the hose? And what happens if the ball moves as a result?**

ANSWER: The hose is artificial and therefore a "movable obstruction." Chip's allowed to move it away. If his ball moves in the process, he must put the ball back without penalty.

Rule 15.2a(1) and definition "Movable Obstruction."

SITUATION: **Chip's making his practice swing too close to the ball ...**

QUESTION: **What's the correct procedure if a player accidentally strikes their ball during a practice swing?**

ANSWER: A practice swing doesn't count as a stroke and can't be declared as such. According to the rules, Chip accidentally caused his ball at rest to move. He incurs 1 penalty stroke and must replace his ball on the original spot. (If the same happens on the green, the ball must again be put back but there's no penalty.)

Rule 9.4b and definition "Stroke."

SITUATION: **Tom's ball is lying on a steep slope short of the green ...**

QUESTION: **Is Tom penalized for causing his ball to move, and where does he play his next stroke from?**

ANSWER: Tom caused his ball to move when he grounded the club. Therefore, he incurs 1 penalty stroke and must put the ball back. If the ball doesn't stay in place on the original spot, Tom must try a second time. If it still doesn't stay at rest, he must place the ball on the nearest spot, not nearer the hole, where it will remain at rest.

Rules 9.4 and 14.2e.

SITUATION: **Chip loves to drive fast ...**

QUESTION: **Is Chip right about dropping a ball under the embedded ball rule?**

ANSWER: No, that rule only applies if a ball's embedded in its own pitch mark. In this case, the ball has been moved and its lie has been altered by an "outside influence." Therefore, Tom must place the ball without penalty on the nearest spot with a lie most similar to the original lie, not nearer the hole and not farther away than 1 club-length.

Rules 9.6, 14.2d(2) and definition "Embedded."

SITUATION: **Tom skulls his tee shot and the ball hits something unexpected ...**

QUESTION: **Where must Tom play his next shot from?**

ANSWER: Tom's ball hit an "outside influence" and was accidentally deflected. That's bad luck. Tom must play the ball as it lies or, in this case, accept 1 penalty stroke and take a drop in accordance with the penalty area rule.

Rules 11.1 and 17.1d.

SITUATION: **Tom's ball lands on top of a mole hill ...**

QUESTION: **Where should Tom play from?**

ANSWER: Tom may play his ball from the mole hill or take free relief as follows. At the nearest point without interference from the mole hill, take a drop within 1 club-length, not nearer the hole.

Rule 16.1b and definition "Animal Hole."

SITUATION: **Tom's ball lands in muddy ground under repair ...**

QUESTION: **Is Tom penalized for cleaning his ball before dropping it?**

ANSWER: When a ball's picked up for a relief procedure and is to be dropped, it may be cleaned, and the player's even allowed to use a new ball. There's no penalty for Tom.

Rules 14.1c and 14.3a.

SITUATION: **Chip's ball lands next to an alligator ...**

QUESTION: **Is Chip allowed to take a free drop?**

ANSWER: Chip may take free relief due to a "dangerous animal condition" as follows. Find the nearest point at a safe distance from the alligator, and drop a ball within 1 club-length, not nearer the hole.

Rule 16.2.

SITUATION: **Chip's ball lands in an area of new grass ...**

QUESTION: **How should Chip proceed?**

ANSWER: In stroke play, if Chip's unsure if he gets free relief, he should play two balls – one ball as it lies and one ball assuming it was lying in ground under repair, i.e., after taking a free drop. However, before doing so, Chip should announce which of the two balls he wishes to count in case both options conform to the rules; and before signing his score card, he must report the case to the Committee, even if he scored the same with both balls. This procedure of playing two balls doesn't exist in match play.

Rules 20.1b(4) and 20.1c(3).

SITUATION: **Chip's club gets stuck in thick grass and accidentally strikes the ball twice ...**

QUESTION: **What's the ruling if the club head accidentally hits the ball twice during a stroke?**

ANSWER: There's no penalty, it counts as one stroke only, and the ball is played as it lies.

Rule 10.1a.

SITUATION: Chip thinks he's a better rally driver than he really is ...

QUESTION: Are Tom and Chip allowed to replace their damaged clubs during the round?

ANSWER: Both Tom and Chip may replace their damaged clubs because the damage was accidental and not caused by abuse. However, they must make sure they don't unreasonably delay play when doing so.

Rules 4.1a(2) and 4.1b(4).

SITUATION: **Tom's ball lands in a flower bed marked as a "No Play Zone" ...**

QUESTION: **Where should Tom play from, and is there a penalty?**

ANSWER: Playing from a no play zone is strictly forbidden. Because the no play zone is marked as ground under repair in this case, Tom must take free relief as follows. At the nearest point without interference from the flower bed, he must drop a ball within 1 club-length, not nearer the hole.

Rules 2.4 and 16.1f.

SITUATION: **Chip's ball is stuck in the middle of a spiky bush ...**

QUESTION: **Does Chip get free relief, and, if so, where does he have to take a drop?**

ANSWER: Although the sprinkler head interferes with Chip's stance, he doesn't get free relief because the lie of his ball is so bad that it's clearly unreasonable to play it as it lies. Chip's best option will be to accept a penalty stroke and to take a drop under the unplayable ball rule.

Rules 16.1a(3) and 19.2.

SITUATION: **While Tom and Chip are playing their round, a thunderstorm approaches ...**

QUESTION: **Will Tom and Chip be penalized for stopping play although there's been no official signal?**

ANSWER: Players are allowed to stop play without penalty if they reasonably believe there's a danger from lightning. They don't have to wait for play to be suspended officially. However, they must report it to the Committee as soon as possible. The ball can be left behind or it can be marked and picked up.

Rule 5.7a.

SITUATION: **Tom and Chip are caught in an unexpected heavy shower on the last holes ...**

QUESTION: **What are Tom's options?**

ANSWER: Tom may play his ball as it lies or take a free drop as follows. At the nearest point without interference from the puddle, drop a ball within 1 club-length, not nearer the hole.

Rule 16.1b and definition "Temporary Water."

SITUATION: Chip's ball lands behind a small bush ...

QUESTION: Does Chip get a free drop for interference from the cart path?

ANSWER: If an immovable artificial object interferes with the player's stance, they're usually entitled to free relief. However, in this case, there's only interference from the cart path because Chip has taken a clearly unreasonable stance. Therefore, he's not entitled to a free drop and the ball is played as it lies.

Rule 16.1a(3).

BUNKER

SITUATION: **Chip's ball is resting against a rake just outside a bunker ...**

QUESTION: **Was Chip allowed to remove the rake? And does he have to play from the bunker, or can he replace his ball?**

ANSWER: The rake is artificial and therefore a "movable obstruction." These may be removed everywhere. If the ball moves as a result, the ball must be put back without penalty. Therefore, Chip isn't just permitted to replace his ball on its original spot, he has to replace it.

Rule 15.2a(1) and definition "Movable Obstruction."

SITUATION: **Tom's preparing for his bunker shot …**

QUESTION: **Is Tom allowed to touch the sand with his club before the stroke?**

ANSWER: Casually leaning on or resting the club in the sand while waiting to play is allowed. However, a player isn't allowed to touch the sand during practice swings, to ground the club behind the ball or to touch the sand during the back swing. Tom gets 2 penalty strokes in stroke play for his practice swing.

Rule 12.2b.

SITUATION: **Chip's ball comes to rest in a large fairway bunker ...**

QUESTION: **Is Chip allowed to rake the bunker before his shot? And if not, what's the penalty?**

ANSWER: Chip doesn't incur a penalty, as he was smoothing the bunker to care for the course. As long as he's not testing the condition of the bunker and not smoothing any prints on his line of play, there's no penalty for raking the sand.

Rule 12.2b(2).

SITUATION: **Tom's ball is lying in a bunker next to a twig ...**

QUESTION: **Is Chip right that a twig mustn't be removed from a bunker?**

ANSWER: A twig is a natural object and therefore a "loose impediment." Loose impediments can be removed everywhere. Tom may remove the twig without penalty. On the other hand, sand and loose soil are not loose impediments and may only be removed on the green.

Rule 15.1a and definition "Loose Impediment."

SITUATION: **Chip thinks he's a great bunker player ...**

QUESTION: **Is Chip allowed to take the ball out of his footprints? Where can he play his next stroke from?**

ANSWER: Chip must play his ball as it lies, or he can declare it unplayable and take a drop. Depending on which of the four dropping options he chooses, he would get 1 or 2 penalty strokes.

Rules 8.1 and 19.3.

SITUATION: Tom and Chip both hit their ball into the same bunker ...

QUESTION: Does Tom have to play the ball as it lies, or is he entitled to relief?

ANSWER: In principle, the ball should always be played as it lies or as it lay when it came to rest. If the conditions for a stroke were altered by another person, the player is entitled to restore them. Therefore, Tom may recreate the original lie – by removing the sand that landed on the ball – without penalty.

Rule 8.1d(1).

SITUATION: **Tom and Chip are on an early morning round after a night of heavy rainfall ...**

QUESTION: **Is Chip allowed to repair the damage in the bunker? Or does he get a free drop? How should he proceed?**

ANSWER: Chip isn't allowed to rake the damaged area around his ball before the stroke. He doesn't get a free drop either unless the bunker was marked as ground under repair. His only options are to play the ball as it lies or to declare it unplayable and take a penalty drop.

Rules 12.2b(1) and 19.3.

SITUATION: **Tom's ball has a bad lie under the lip of a bunker ...**

QUESTION: **May Tom drop his ball outside the bunker when taking unplayable ball relief back on the line?**

ANSWER: Yes. There are four dropping options when declaring a ball unplayable in a bunker. Dropping back on the line is possible inside as well as outside of the bunker. If the ball is dropped inside the bunker, the penalty is 1 stroke whereas if dropped outside of the bunker, the penalty is 2 strokes.

Rule 19.3.

SITUATION: **Tom hits a long shot from a bunker ...**

QUESTION: **Where does Tom have to play from, and what's the correct procedure?**

ANSWER: Tom must drop a ball within 1 club-length of the spot where he played his last stroke, not nearer the hole, under penalty of 1 stroke. However, he may smooth the sand before dropping.

Rules 18.2b and 12.2b(3).

PENALTY AREA

SITUATION: **Chip's ball lands on a grass bank inside a penalty area ...**

QUESTION: **When playing a stroke from within a penalty area, is grounding the club behind the ball allowed or not?**

ANSWER: Grounding the club in a penalty area and even setting it down in the water is permitted. When playing a ball as it lies from a penalty area, the same rules apply as in the general area. In the bunker, however, grounding the club in the sand behind the ball isn't allowed.

Rules 17.1b and 12.2b(1).

SITUATION: **Tom's ball comes to rest in a creek between branches and leaves ...**

QUESTION: **Does Tom get a penalty or not? And how must he proceed?**

ANSWER: "Loose impediments" such as unattached leaves and branches may be removed everywhere without penalty. However, if the ball moves as a result, it must be put back with 1 penalty stroke (except on the green where it's without penalty). Because Tom wasn't cautious enough when removing the leaves from the penalty area, he gets 1 penalty stroke; he must put his ball back, but not the leaves.

Rule 15.1 and definition "Loose Impediment."

SITUATION: **Tom's ball is lying just inside a red penalty area ...**

QUESTION: **May Tom remove the red stake before playing his ball from within the penalty area?**

ANSWER: Red and yellow stakes are "movable obstructions" and may be removed without penalty. However, it's important to put them back in exactly the same spot in order that the markings are the same for all players.

Rule 15.2 and definition "Obstruction."

SITUATION: **Chip's ball comes to rest on the steep bank of a pond ...**

QUESTION: **Is Chip penalized for moving his ball when he fell, and where does he have to play from?**

ANSWER: Chip is penalized 1 stroke for moving his ball at rest, and he must replace the ball on its original spot. If the original ball can't be found, he may substitute another ball.

Rules 9.4b and 14.2a.

SITUATION: **Tom's ball disappears into a lake ...**

QUESTION: **What are Tom's dropping options as his ball is in the yellow penalty area?**

ANSWER: Under penalty of 1 stroke, Tom can take a drop at the spot of his last stroke. Also with 1 penalty stroke, he can take a drop back on the line going from the hole through the entry point where the ball last crossed the edge of the penalty area. Dropping within 2 club-lengths from the entry point is only an option if the ball is in a red penalty area.

Rule 17.1d.

SITUATION: **Tom has an easy shot over a lake, but his nerves fail ...**

> THAT'S THE THING WITH WATER - YOU SHOULD TAKE ONE MORE CLUB BUT YOU CAN ALSO TAKE ONE MORE BALL.

> VERY FUNNY ...

> I'LL TAKE A DROP IN THE DROP ZONE OVER THERE.

> YOU CAN'T DO THAT. IT'D BE MUCH CLOSER TO THE HOLE.

QUESTION: **May Tom drop a ball in the drop zone if it's nearer the hole than where his ball entered the water?**

ANSWER: In the case of penalty areas, the rules provide several dropping options, each with 1 penalty stroke. As an additional option, the Committee may provide special drop zones by local rule. With 1 penalty stroke, Tom may drop a ball inside the specially marked drop zone, even though it's nearer the hole than where his ball last crossed the edge of the penalty area. The Committee may position drop zones wherever they think they're most appropriate.

Rule MLR E-1.

SITUATION: **Tom's tee shot is heading towards a lake ...**

QUESTION: **May Tom play a provisional ball if he believes his first ball is in the penalty area?**

ANSWER: A provisional ball may only be played if the original ball could be lost outside a penalty area or out of bounds. The rules prohibit playing a provisional ball if the original ball has come to rest in a penalty area. Tom's second ball is his new ball in play under penalty of 1 stroke, even if he finds his first ball in a playable position.

Rule 18.3a.

OUT OF BOUNDS
PROVISIONAL BALL
LOST BALL

SITUATION: **Tom's ball lands very close to a fence that defines out of bounds ...**

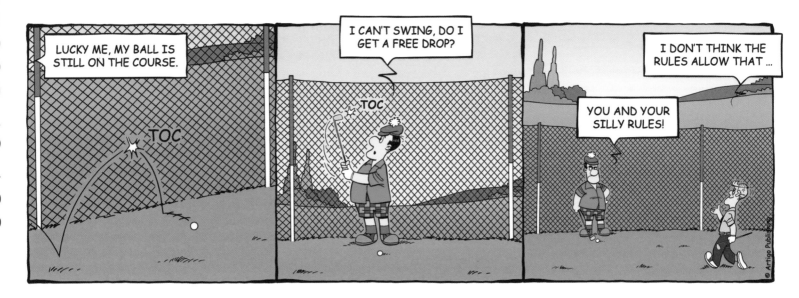

QUESTION: **Does Tom get a free drop because the out of bounds fence interferes with his swing?**

ANSWER: If a fixed artificial object ("immovable obstruction") interferes with a player's stance or swing, they usually get free relief. However, objects that mark out of bounds or artificial installations that are located out of bounds don't fall under this rule. Tom must play his ball as it lies or take a drop under the unplayable ball rule with 1 penalty stroke.

Rules 16.1 and 19.2.

SITUATION: **Chip's ball goes straight out of bounds ...**

QUESTION: **Is Chip allowed to drop a ball with 1 penalty stroke within 2 club-lengths of where the ball went out of bounds?**

ANSWER: No, unless a local rule allows another procedure, the standard procedure for a ball that's out of bounds is as follows. With 1 penalty stroke, return to the spot of the last stroke and take a drop within 1 club-length, not nearer the hole (you can tee up in the teeing area). If Chip dropped and played as in the above image, he'd have to correct his error otherwise he'd be disqualified.

Rules 18.2b and 14.7.

SITUATION: **Tom's ball comes to rest close to out of bounds ...**

QUESTION: **Is Chip right about the penalty? And what if Tom puts the stake back?**

ANSWER: Chip's right that removing objects defining out of bounds is not permitted. If Tom plays under the improved conditions, he'll incur 2 penalty strokes in stroke play. However, if Tom replaces the stake before playing his stroke, there's no penalty.

Rules 8.1a and 8.1c.

SITUATION: **Tom's first tee shot has landed in the woods ...**

QUESTION: **Does a player have to mention the word "provisional" when announcing that they're going to play a provisional ball?**

ANSWER: A player should use the word "provisional" to clearly indicate their intention. Just saying "another one" or "one more" isn't sufficient, even if under the given circumstances playing a provisional would be the most sensible course of action. If a ball isn't properly announced as provisional, it becomes the new ball in play with 1 penalty stroke.

Rule 18.3b.

SITUATION: **After a bad tee shot, Tom plays a provisional ball ...**

QUESTION: **Is Tom allowed to continue play with one of the balls, or are they both considered lost?**

ANSWER: If a ball can't be identified, it's usually considered lost. However, in this special case both balls belong to the same player. Therefore, Tom must choose one of the balls and treat it as his provisional ball, i.e., it becomes the ball in play with 1 penalty stroke. Tom will be hitting his 4th shot.

Rule 18.3c(2).

SITUATION: **Chip slices his drive into the rough ...**

QUESTION: **Is Chip allowed to continue with his provisional ball?**

ANSWER: If the original ball has been found within 3 minutes, Chip must abandon the provisional ball and play his original ball without penalty (2nd shot). Otherwise, he would be playing a wrong ball.

Rules 18.3c(3) and 6.3c(1).

SITUATION: Tom and Chip are searching for Chip's ball in high grass ...

QUESTION: What happens if Chip continues play with his ball which was found after a search time of 3 minutes?

ANSWER: After a search time of 3 minutes has elapsed, a ball is considered lost. If Chip played this "lost" ball, he'd be playing a wrong ball. The stroke wouldn't count but he'd get 2 penalty strokes in stroke play. Furthermore, he'd need to correct his mistake by playing again from the spot of his previous stroke with 1 penalty stroke, otherwise, he'd be disqualified in stroke play.

Rules 6.3c(1), 18.2b and definition "Lost."

SITUATION: Tom and Chip's shots land close together ...

QUESTION: What's the correct procedure if Tom and Chip can't identify their balls?

ANSWER: If two identical balls are found in the same area, and it's not clear which ball belongs to whom, both balls are considered lost. Tom and Chip must return to the spot of their previous strokes and re-play with 1 penalty stroke.

Rules 7.2 and 18.2a(1).

SITUATION: **Chip's ball has landed in the rough where it's hard to find ...**

QUESTION: **If Chip finds his ball after 2 ½ minutes and then loses sight of it, how much search time does he then have to find it again?**

ANSWER: A player is allowed a total of 3 minutes to find their ball. If a ball is found and then lost as in the above scenario, the clock stops when the ball is found but it doesn't start over when the ball is lost again. Chip has 30 seconds left to find his ball before it's considered lost.

Rule 18.2a(1) and interpretation 18.2a(1)/1.

SITUATION: **Tom's convinced that he hit a good shot but ...**

QUESTION: **What's the correct procedure for Tom?**

ANSWER: As long as Tom hasn't seen anybody stealing his ball, he simply has 3 minutes to find it. After this time has elapsed, the ball is lost and Tom must, with 1 penalty stroke, return to the spot of his previous stroke and drop a ball within 1 club-length, not nearer the hole (he may tee up in the teeing area).

Rule 18.2.

SITUATION: **Although he hit a good shot on a Par 3, Chip can't find his ball ...**

QUESTION: **Did Chip score a hole-in-one or was the ball lost and he has to finish the hole with his second ball?**

ANSWER: Chip's first ball counts as a hole-in-one. The hole was completed when the ball came to rest in the hole. There's no penalty for playing another ball.

Rule 6.5.

GREEN AND FRINGE

SITUATION: **Tom wants to use his lucky putting ball ...**

QUESTION: **May Tom change the ball before holing out?**

ANSWER: Substituting the ball during play of a hole isn't permitted unless the rules explicitly allow it, e.g. when taking relief. If Tom played the substituted ball, his stroke would count, but he'd incur 1 penalty stroke.

Rule 6.3b(3).

SITUATION: Tom's ball is farther away from the hole, but Chip's ball is still off the green …

QUESTION: Who plays first, and if a player plays in the wrong order, is there a penalty?

ANSWER: It's Tom's turn to play. The ball that's farther from the hole is played first, regardless of whether it's on or off the green. If Chip played first, there would be no penalty. However, in match play, Tom would be entitled to cancel Chip's stroke and ask him to replay in the correct order.

Rules 6.4a and 6.4b.

SITUATION: **Tom plays an approach shot and his ball hits Chip's ball …**

QUESTION: **Does Chip's ball count as holed? And does Tom get a penalty? What's the ruling?**

ANSWER: Chip didn't score a birdie. He must take his ball out of the hole and put it back on its original spot. Tom must play his ball as it lies. There's no penalty for Tom as he played from off the green.

Rules 9.6 and 11.1.

SITUATION: **Chip tops his approach shot ...**

QUESTION: **Where does Chip have to play from, and is there a penalty?**

ANSWER: If, after a stroke from off the green, the ball is deliberately deflected by a person, the player must estimate where the ball would've come to rest and drop a ball within 1 club-length from that estimated spot, not nearer the hole. In this case, Chip will have to take a drop in the bunker. Tom incurs a 2-stroke penalty in stroke play for deliberately deflecting Chip's ball.

Rules 11.2b and 11.2c(1).

SITUATION: **Tom's ball is lying on the fringe, and he would like to putt ...**

QUESTION: **Is Chip right or may Tom repair both pitch-marks?**

ANSWER: In principle, the player may not improve their line of play, except for on the green where repairing damage is permitted. Therefore, Tom may repair pitch-marks and spike marks on the green but not off the green, e.g. on the fringe.

Rules 8.1a and 13.1c(2).

SITUATION: **Tom and Chip arrive on a green that's full of leaves ...**

QUESTION: **Is Tom allowed to use a leaf blower to remove the leaves? What about the anti-slice pills?**

ANSWER: Detached leaves and branches are "loose impediments" and may be removed anywhere on the course, in any way. This is allowed without penalty as long as it doesn't cause an unreasonable delay. Tom may remove the leaves using his hand, his foot, a club, a towel or even a leaf blower. Regarding the anti-slice pills – please ask your local pro!

Rule 15.1a.

SITUATION: **Chip has marked and lifted his ball on the green and is about to put it back ...**

QUESTION: **Is there a penalty if, on the green, the ball isn't replaced on exactly the same spot that it was lifted from?**

ANSWER: A ball that has been marked and lifted must be replaced on its original spot. If Chip didn't replace his ball on the correct spot, he would be playing from a wrong place even if the spot was only one inch away. The stroke would count but he would get 2 penalty strokes in stroke play.

Rules 13.1b, 14.2c and 14.7.

SITUATION: **Tom and Chip are playing golf in the pouring rain ...**

QUESTION: **Is using an umbrella while making a stroke permitted?**

ANSWER: Protecting oneself against the elements by holding an umbrella as Tom did while putting is permitted. However, accepting protection against the elements from another person, such as having someone hold an umbrella over your head while making a stroke, isn't allowed. Chip gets 2 penalty strokes in stroke play for accepting this kind of help.

Rule 10.2b(5).

SITUATION: **Tom has only a short putt left ...**

QUESTION: **Does Tom have to replay the stroke, and is there a penalty?**

ANSWER: The stroke counts and the ball is holed. However, Tom incurs a 2-stroke penalty in stroke play for not fairly striking the ball (not with the club head).

Rule 10.1a and definition "Stroke."

SITUATION: **Tom's preparing for his putt when a mishap occurs ...**

QUESTION: **How must Tom proceed, and is there a penalty?**

ANSWER: On the green, accidentally causing your own ball at rest to move (e.g. when grounding the club or taking a practice swing) doesn't incur a penalty, while in other parts of the course it often does. Tom must put his ball back without penalty.

Rule 13.1d(1).

SITUATION: **Tom messes up a very simple putt ...**

QUESTION: **How do you count a ball that's knocked away in anger? And where does Tom have to play his next stroke from?**

ANSWER: Hitting a ball away from the hole in anger isn't considered a stroke and doesn't count. According to the rules, Tom deliberately caused his ball at rest to move. Therefore, he must put it back on the original spot with 1 penalty stroke. If the ball can't be recovered, Tom may take another ball without an additional penalty stroke for unallowed substitution of the ball being counted in this case.

Rules 1.3c(4), 6.3b(3), 9.4b, 14.2a and definition "Stroke."

SITUATION: **Chip leaves his putt just a little short ...**

QUESTION: **How long may Chip wait for the ball to fall into the hole?**

ANSWER: Chip's allowed a reasonable time to reach the hole and then 10 more seconds to wait and see whether the ball will fall into the hole. If the ball falls in within 10 seconds, it's considered holed. If it falls in after 10 seconds, it's also considered holed but the player will get 1 penalty stroke, i.e., it doesn't make sense to wait longer than 10 seconds.

Rule 13.3a.

SITUATION: **Tom's ball is wedged between the lip of the hole and the flagstick ...**

QUESTION: **When's a ball considered holed?**

ANSWER: When a ball's resting against the flagstick in the hole, if any part of the ball is below the surface of the green, the ball is considered holed. Tom's ball is holed, it's not necessary for all of it to be below the surface of the green.

Rule 13.2c.

MATCH PLAY AND OTHER FORMS OF PLAY

SITUATION: **During match play, Tom plays first when it's actually Chip's turn ...**

QUESTION: **Is Tom penalized, and does he have to replay in the correct order?**

ANSWER: In principle, if a player plays out of turn, there's no penalty. Therefore, Tom isn't penalized in this case. However, in match play, Chip as the opponent is entitled to cancel Tom's stroke and ask him to replay in the correct order.

Rules 6.4a and 6.4b.

SITUATION: **During match play, Chip tees off in front of the tee markers ...**

QUESTION: **Is there a penalty, or can Chip continue to play the ball as it lies?**

ANSWER: In match play, there's no penalty and the stroke counts. However, Tom as the opponent may cancel the stroke and require Chip to tee off again correctly. (In stroke play, the stroke wouldn't count, Chip would get 2 penalty strokes, and he'd have to tee off again from within the teeing area.)

Rule 6.1b and definition "Teeing Area."

SITUATION: **During match play, Chip's about to take a drop from a red penalty area ...**

QUESTION: **Is it permissible to change a rule in match play if both players agree to it?**

ANSWER: If players deliberately agree to change or ignore a rule they know applies, they're disqualified. This is valid in both stroke play and match play.

Rules 1.3b(1) and 3.2d(4).

SITUATION: **During match play, Tom putts too hard and his ball rolls past the hole ...**

QUESTION: **What's the correct ruling in match play?**

ANSWER: There's no penalty for either player. If, after a stroke from the green, the ball hits another ball on the green, there's no penalty in match play (2 penalty strokes for Tom in stroke play). Chip must put his ball back and Tom must play his as it lies.

Rules 11.1 and 9.6.

SITUATION: **During match play, Tom has a very short putt left to tie the hole ...**

QUESTION: **Does the concession count or is it invalid because Tom decided to putt anyway?**

ANSWER: The concession counts, and Tom's ball is considered holed. A concession in match play is final and can't be withdrawn or declined.

Rule 3.2b(2).

SITUATION: **During match play, Chip holes an important putt ...**

QUESTION: **Has Tom lost the hole because he picked up his ball already, or can he go back and hole out?**

ANSWER: Tom won the hole and doesn't need to hole out. In match play, if a player gives their opponent wrong information about the strokes they've taken (including penalty strokes) and they don't correct this before the opponent plays their next stroke or takes a similar action (such as picking up the ball), they lose the hole.

Rule 3.2d(1).

SITUATION: **Tom and Chip are playing in a Stableford competition ...**

THAT'S NOT MY BALL ... I MUST'VE PLAYED THE WRONG BALL SOMEWHERE ON THE WAY.

YOU HAVE TO GO BACK AND PLAY THE CORRECT BALL.

IT'S STABLEFORD, I'LL JUST GIVE UP THE HOLE AND PLAY AGAIN ON THE NEXT.

I THINK YOU HAVE TO CORRECT YOUR MISTAKE, OTHERWISE YOU'RE DISQUALIFIED.

QUESTION: **What's the ruling in a Stableford competition – is Tom disqualified if he doesn't rectify his mistake and hole out with the correct ball?**

ANSWER: In Stableford, it's not mandatory to always hole out. Tom will simply get zero points for the hole. To help the pace of play, giving up a hole where zero points would be scored is encouraged.

Rule 21.1c.

S I T U A T I O N : **Tom and Chip are playing in a foursome competition ...**

Q U E S T I O N : **Is Tom permitted to deliberately miss the ball so Chip can play next?**

A N S W E R : If Tom didn't intend to strike the ball, there's not been a stroke and it's still Tom's turn to play. If Chip played out of turn, the stroke wouldn't count, the team would incur 2 penalty strokes in stroke play and they'd have to correct the mistake by having Tom play again in the correct order.

Rule 22.3 and definition "Stroke."

SITUATION: **Tom and Chip are partners in a four-ball competition ...**

QUESTION: **With a four-ball, is it necessary that both partners are present at the start or throughout the round?**

ANSWER: In four-ball, only one score counts, therefore the team may be represented by one partner during all or part of the round.

Rule 23.4.

SITUATION: Chip's playing in a team competition and receiving help from his coach ...

QUESTION: In a team competition, may the designated "advice giver" stand behind Chip while he putts?

ANSWER: A coach, just like a caddie or a partner, isn't allowed to be standing on an extension of the line of play when the player begins to take their stance and until the stroke is made. Since the coach didn't move away, Chip is penalized 2 strokes in stroke play.

Rules 24.4a and 10.2b(4).

Rules Index

This book conforms to the official "Rules of Golf", published by the USGA/R&A and effective as of 01.01.2023.

Perfect for looking up the rules – the "Golf Rules Quick Reference" pocket guide and the "iGolfrules" iPhone app.

Golf Rules Quick Reference

A practical guide for use on the course.

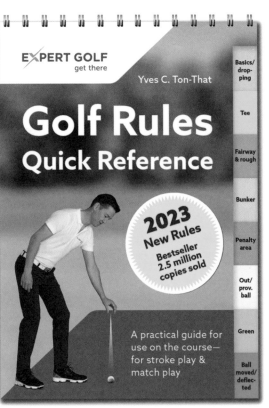

- 48 pages
- 180+ colored illustrations
- Pocket-sized
- Spiral-bound
- Weatherproof
- Multi award-winning
- Recommended by golf associations
- Conforms to USGA/ R&A rules
- ISBN 978-3-906852-39-3

iGolfrules

Answers your rules questions in a matter of seconds – you will find the right solution with a maximum of 3 clicks.

Recommended by Apple.
Available from the iTunes App Store.